The Healthy Cook's
Kitchen Companion

AN ORGANIZER
FOR *YOUR*
FAVORITE RECIPES

With witty food for thought and illustrations from
VEGETARIANA and *AMERICAN HARVEST* by
Nava Atlas

AMBERWOOD PRESS
New Paltz, NY

Illustrations that appear on these pages are from:

Vegetariana: A Rich Harvest of Wit, Lore and Recipes (revised edition)
by Nava Atlas ⓒ 1993, Little, Brown and Co.

And:

American Harvest: Regional Recipes for the Vegetarian Kitchen (2nd edition)
by Nava Atlas ⓒ 1991, Amberwood Press

AMBERWOOD PRESS
65 Prospect Street
New Paltz, NY 12561-1143

Printed in the United States of America

10 9 8 7 6 5 4 3 2 1

CONTENTS

SOUPS

Correct way to finish soup: Licking the bowl is both quiet & dignified.

"Many cooks do not appear to be alive to the fact that the less pretentious they make a soup, the more certain it is to give satisfaction, and of all cooking, nothing is easier to do well, and nothing is more difficult to do badly, than soup-making—too much pains being productive of the same results as too many cooks."

—*Godey's Lady's Book,* 1870

"Whoever tells a lie cannot be pure in heart—and only the pure in heart can make a good soup."

—Ludwig van Beethoven, in an 1817 letter

"In taking soup, it is necessary to avoid lifting too much into the spoon, or filling the mouth so full as to almost stop the breath."

—St. John the Baptist de la Salle
  The Rules of Christian Manners and Civility, 1695

SALADS & DRESSINGS

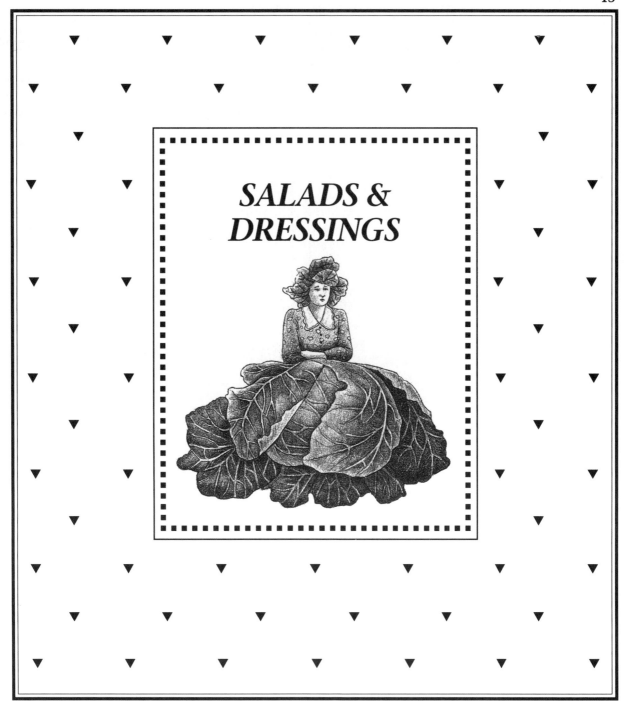

"You can put everything, and the more things the better, into a salad, as into a conversation; but everything depends upon the skill of mixing."
—Charles Dudley Warner
    My Summer in a Garden, 1871

"If possible, when combining vegetables, have those which are of a delicate flavor form the body of a salad, using only a small proportion of those with strong flavor."

—Maria Parloa
Miss Parloa's Kitchen Companion, 1887

_____

"To make a good salad is to be a brilliant diplomat: one must know exactly how much oil one must put with one's vinegar."

—Oscar Wilde (1856-1900)

The goddess of oil & vinegar

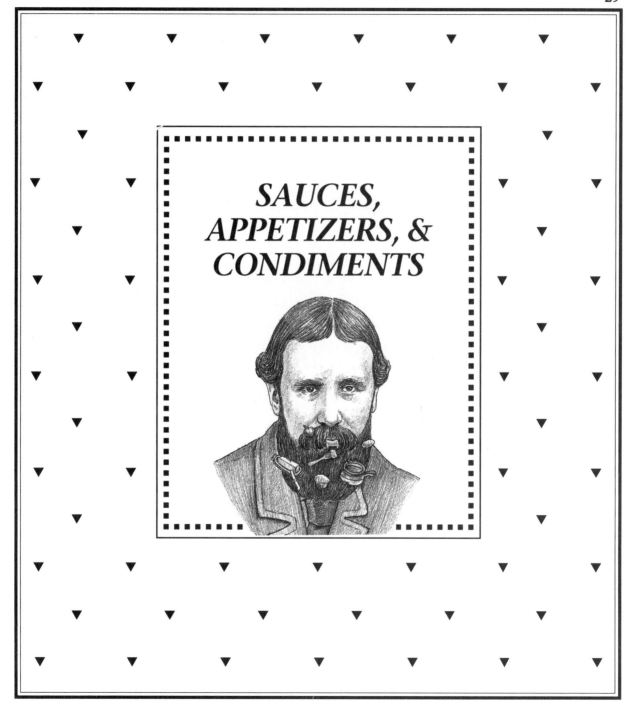

SAUCES, APPETIZERS, & CONDIMENTS

The dictionary tells us that "sauce," as a verb, means "to add zest to," and that the word also gives us "saucy," meaning alternatively, "pert" or "impudent." This interpretation aside, sauce must be associated with something worth reaching for, as we are told that "what is sauce for the goose is sauce for the gander.

A Saucy Little Girl

"There is no garden herb comes near unto parsley, as well for toothsomeness as for health."

—William Vaughn
Directions for Health, 1617

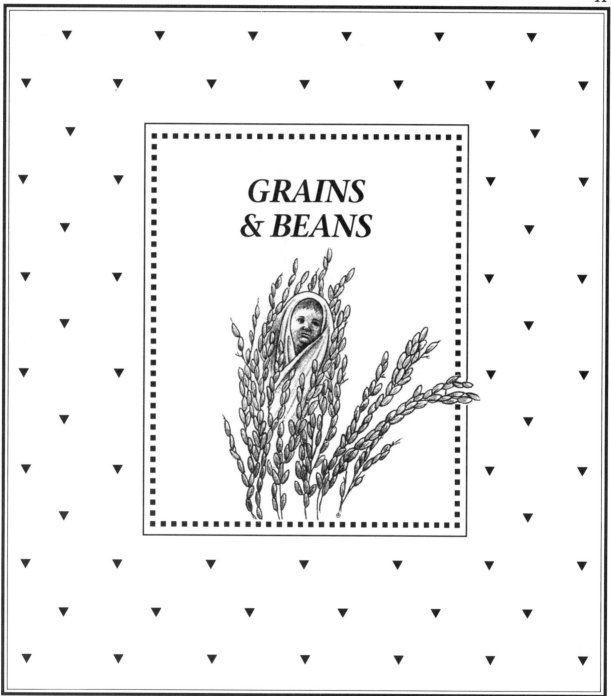

GRAINS & BEANS

_____

Did you ever wonder why beans have seams? In Grimm's Fairy Tales, a bean laughs so hard at the demise of her friends the Straw and the Coal that her sides split. A kind tailor passing by spots her and sews her sides back together. Ever since, beans have had seams.

"That's the bean called pink, called frijole, called the Mexican strawberry."

—*This Week Magazine,* March 1949

pink

frijole

Mexican Strawberry

"The Goddess ov korn iz also the Goddess ov oats, and barley, and bukwheat. Her name is Series, she is a mithological woman, and like menny wimmen now a daze, she is hard tew lokate."

—Josh Billings
His Works, Complete, 1876

_____

"As much alike as if they'd
been kidney beans, shelled
out of the same pod."
—Ann S. Stephens
High Life in New York, 1844

"One grain fills not the sack, but helps his fellows."

—George Herbert
Jacula Prudentum,
1640

PASTA

"Macaroni,,

"Music is like spaghetti. If you like spaghetti, you do not eat it morning, noon, and night. You only have it once in a while. It should be kept distant so that you have a real hunger for it."

—Dimitri Mitropoulos, quoted by Giuseppe Prezzolini
Spaghetti Dinner, 1955

"Don't be intimidated by foreign cookery. Tomatoes and oregano make it Italian. Wine and tarragon make it French. Sour cream makes it Russian. Lemon and cinnamon make it Greek. Soy sauce makes it Chinese. Garlic makes it good. Now you are an International Cook."

—Alice May Brock
Alice's Restaurant Cookbook, 1969

During the 1700s, when an English soldier wrote the lyrics of "Yankee Doodle Dandy," macaroni was new to England and quickly became quite a fashionable food. Hence, anything stylish, whether clothing, food, music, manners, or a feather in one's cap, was called "macaroni," so positive was the connotation of the word.

Your hat is so simple, yet so smart, and so very, very Macaroni!

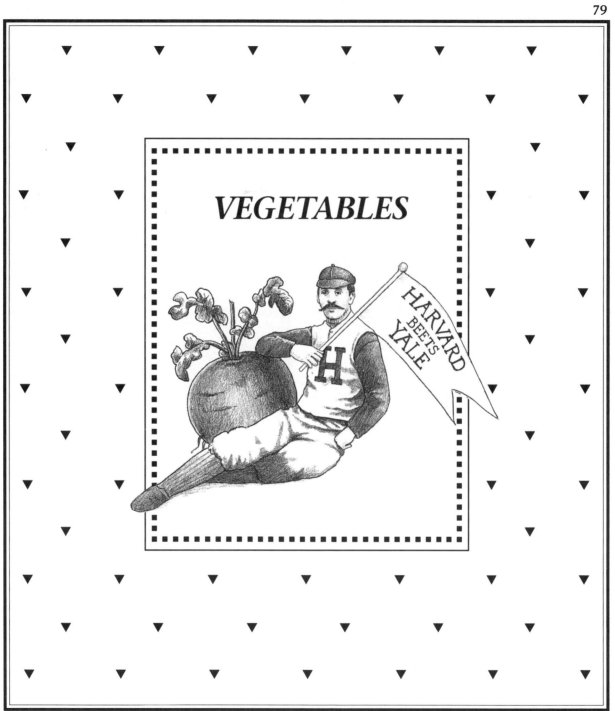

A Most Handsome Vegetable

"[The cauliflower] is a handsome and delicate vegetable. It is a pity that more people do not know how to cook it properly."

—Maria Parloa
Miss Parloa's Kitchen Companion, 1887

In European folk-
lore, it was believed
that potatoes should
be planted on starry
nights so that they'd
have many eyes.

"To have peas in perfection, they must be quite young, gathered early in the morning, kept in a cool place, and not shelled until they are ready to be dressed."
—Mary Randolph
The Virginia Housewife, 1824

"Pray, how does your asparagus perform?"

—John Adams (1735-1826), in a letter to his wife, Abigail

PERFORMING NOW FROM THE HOME GARDEN

LIVE ASPARAGUS!

TOFU, TEMPEH, & OTHER SOY FOODS

"Go bump your head against the corner of a cake of tofu" is a Japanese expression meaning "Get lost!"

A Chinese saying describes a hopeless situation as one that is "as futile as trying to clamp two pieces of tofu together."

BREAKFAST & LUNCH FOODS

"Women are going wild over the pancake hat."
—*Kansas City Times*, Sept. 1931

"The servant will bring you hot muffins and corn battercakes every two
minutes."
—*Maryland Historical Magazine*, 1833

"O dear! How can I tell it. Squash again for breakfast."

—Diary of a Pioneer Woman

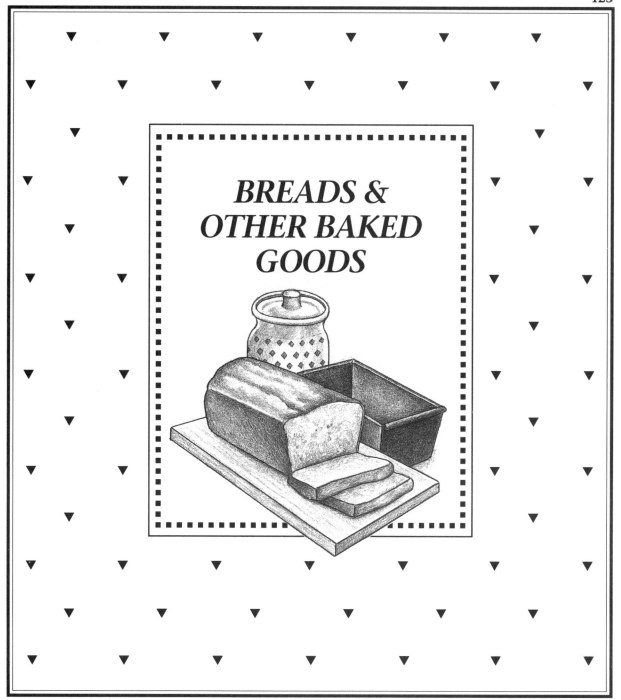

BREADS & OTHER BAKED GOODS

Bread is better than the song of birds.
—Danish proverb

It is not proper to shock your guests by serving them thin bread at dinner.

"At family dinners, where the common household bread is used, it should never be cut less than an inch and a half thick. There is nothing more plebeian than *thin* bread at dinner.

—Charles Day
  Hints on Etiquette, 1843

_____

"The Indians make their bread of the
Indian Corn, wild Oats, or the Seed of
the Sunflower.
—Robert Beverly
   The History and Present State of Virginia, 1705

DESSERTS & FRUIT

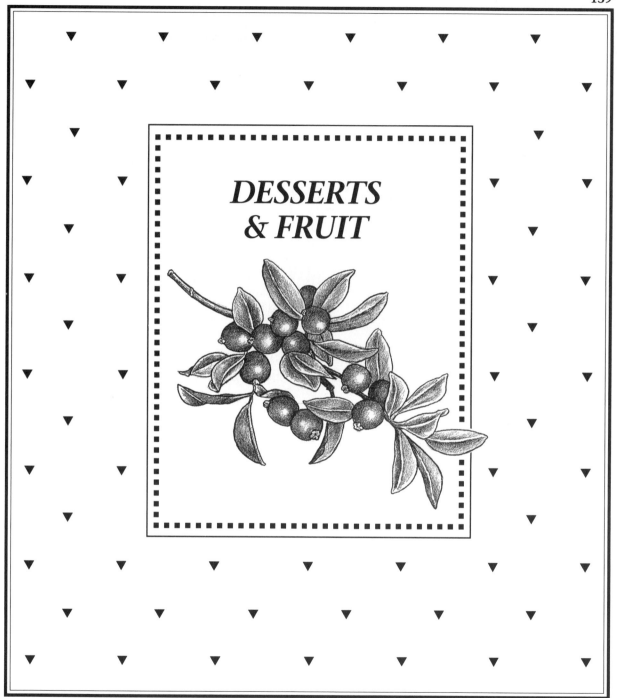

Better one bite of the peach of immortality than a whole basket of apricots.
—Chinese Proverb

"There is no love sincerer than the love of food."

—George Bernard Shaw
Man and Superman, 1903

**I hope before I'm through
To eat my cake and bake it, too.**

—Margaret Fishback
Career Girl, 1940

"All the woods, fields and gardens are full of strawberries, which grow excellently well in this beautiful and lovely land."

—William Byrd
Natural History of Virginia, 1737

OTHER TITLES FROM AMBERWOOD PRESS

AMERICAN HARVEST
Regional Recipes for the Vegetarian Kitchen
by Nava Atlas

American Harvest delves into our wonderful culinary history to assemble a wide array of sumptuous, classic dishes. Regional favorites such as Banana-Pecan Pancakes from New Orleans, Black Bean Tostadas from New Mexico, and Pennsylvania Dutch Corn Noodles are prepared with wholesome ingredients and accompanied by delectable bits of Americana and whimsically rendered illustrations.

Paperback ❏ Illustrated ❏ 191 pages ❏ $11.95

SOUPS FOR ALL SEASONS
Bountiful Vegetarian Soups
by Nava Atlas

Here is a collection of soups to suit every taste, any time of year. These meatless soups are low in fat but rich in flavor—brimming with the bounty of each season. You'll find exotic international favorites, basic comfort soups, elegant broths and plenty of hearty meals-in-a-bowl. And to add a great finishing touch, there's also a selection of accompaniments to make—muffins, dumplings, biscuits and more.

Paperback ❏ Illustrated ❏ 128 pages ❏ $9.95

THE IDEA BOOK
A Journal for Creative Thinkers

This unique journal is designed for creative individuals to record and define their flashes of inspiration, and is embellished with inspirational quotes on innovation, creativity, and the power of thought. *The Idea Book* also includes a brief resource guide to help develop and market ideas. A useful tool and valuable keepsake for artists, writers, inventors, entrepreneurs, and a choice gift item for anyone with creative spirit!

Hardcover ❏ Illustrated ❏ 112 pages ❏ $12.95

Available at bookstores, natural food stores and gift shops everywhere.
For more information, write to us at:
AMBERWOOD PRESS
65 Prospect Street
New Paltz, NY 12561-1143
(914) 255-3597